Merrill *Linguistic* Readers

READER 4

Charles C. Fries

International Lecturer in Linguistics
Professor of English and Linguistics, Emeritus, University of Michigan

Agnes C. Fries

Consultant

Rosemary G. Wilson

Assistant Director in Charge of Reading, Curriculum Office
School District of Philadelphia, Pennsylvania

Mildred K. Rudolph

Consulting Teacher, Curriculum Office
School District of Philadelphia, Pennsylvania

CHARLES E. MERRILL PUBLISHING CO.
A BELL & HOWELL COMPANY
Columbus, Ohio 43216

TABLE OF CONTENTS

Copyright 1966 by CHARLES E. MERRILL PUBLISHING CO.
A Bell & Howell Company   Columbus, Ohio 43216

Printed in the United States of America

ISBN 0-675-01324-0

shop

shot

ship

shut

shed

shell

shack

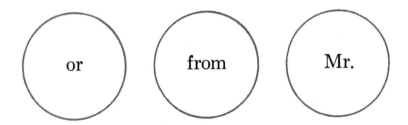

ketchup

The Little Shop

Dan's mother and dad had let him go to Grandma and Grandpa's for a bit. Rags was with him, and Dan had lots of fun. Then Grandma had to go to the shop for a mop and a pot.

Grandma went to Grandpa for a check. She got the check from him and tucked it into her big bag. "Good-by," she said to Grandpa and Dan.

"I will go with you to shop," said Dan.

Dan and Grandma had to pass by a little shack to get to the shop. Dan said, "Is that a woodshed?"

"It's a shed or shack, but it's not for wood," said Grandma.

"Let's look in," said Dan.

"We can't. It's shut and locked," said Grandma. "Let's go on to the shop, Dan. It's such a good little shop! It has —

"A little bit of this
And a little bit of that,
A good wood bat
And a tan sun hat,
A box with lots of shells
And a cat with ten tin bells,
Thick pads for cots,
Little ships for tots.
Nutmeg!
Ketchup!
Napkins!
Bits of this and bits of that!"

"Good!" said Dan. "Let's go, Grandma!"

At the Shop

Dan and Grandma went into the shop. Dan said, "Grandma, I will get this box with the shells on top for my mother."

"Good," said Grandma.

"And that jug with a little ship in it for Dad," he said.

"No, not that jug, Dan," she said. "It has a chip in it."

"Then I will get him this red bag that zips. His lunch will fit in it," said Dan.

"Yes, his lunch will fit, but it will get hot in the bag," said Grandma.

"Well," Dan said, "I will get him this big matchbox."

But the matchbox did not shut. So then Grandma and Dan took it to Mr. Woods, the man in the shop. Mr. Woods said to Dan, "Yes, I can fix it for you, my little lad."

Mr. Woods fixed the box, and Grandma said, "You are in luck, Dan. You have a box for your mother and a box for your dad."

Then Dan looked at this and looked at that. He ran a little van. He shot a peg from a little gun. And he looked and looked at a little tin chick that pecks.

Grandma got her mop and the pot. She got the little tin chick. "You can have it for a kiss and a hug," she said to Dan. So Dan got the tin chick.

Then the man said, "It's six. I have to shut my shop."

"Six!" said Grandma. "Let's go, Dan. We have to get back to Grandpa."

"Good-by," said Dan to the man in the shop. "This is a good shop, but we have to go."

"Good-by, Mr. Woods. We will be back," Grandma said.

fish

wish

dish

rash

hash

mash

cash

Lunch for Rags

Grandma had to fix lunch for Dan and Grandpa. "I will mash bits of this fish in a dish," she said. "It's codfish."

Dan said, "That's not a good lunch for me, Grandma. I get a rash from fish. Then I itch."

"Well," Grandma said, "you can have ham hash if you wish. I can mash a yam and fix it with bits of ham."

"That will be good," Dan said.

So Dan had ham hash for his lunch, and Grandma and Grandpa had codfish hash. But Rags had bits of fish from Grandpa's dish. Then he had ham hash from Dan's dish. Rags had a good lunch!

A Bag to Pack

Sid had to go by Grandma and Grandpa's on Dad's van. "Tell them that we miss Dan," Dad said as Sid got on the van.

Sid did tell Grandpa, but Grandma was at the shop with Dan. So Sid said good-by to Grandpa and went back on the van.

Grandma and Dan got back from the shop with six bags and a box. Grandpa went and took the bags from Grandma. He said to her, "Dan's mother and dad miss him. Sid said so. Dan has to go back to them."

Grandma was sad, but she kissed Dan and said, "I will go up and pack your bag for you, Dan."

"Dan is big. Let him do it," Grandpa

said. "Then you and I can go to the bus with him."

"Yes, I can do it," Dan said, and he went to pack his bag.

Then Rags ran and got his red wood peg. He took it to Dan for him to tuck into the bag. Dan looked at Rags and said, "It is fun to be with Grandma and Grandpa, but I did miss Mother and Dad. And I did miss Pam and Tim and Jim and Bud. Tell me, Rags, did you miss Nat and Little Tom? I bet you did!"

Then Dan tucked the red peg into his bag and took the bag to Grandpa. "I am packed, and Rags is packed," he said. "Let's go, Grandpa!"

At the Bus Shed

Dan's grandma and grandpa took him to catch the bus. Grandpa had to cash a check at the bus shed.

Grandma looked sad. She said, "Dan, I wish you did not have to go. Grandpa and I will miss you."

Dan kissed her and said, "Do not be sad, Grandma. I will be back." Then he got into the bus with Rags.

The man on the bus had to fit Dan's bag up on top. Then he ran the bus.

Dan looked back from the bus. "Good-by, good-by!" he yelled at Grandma and Grandpa. Then the bus took him back to his mother and dad.

rang	ring
hang	sing
sang	king
bang	wing
	thing
long	
song	hung
	rung

Back With Mother and Dad

Dad met Dan at the bus. He took Dan's bag and he took Rags. Dan took the big matchbox and the box with the shells. Then he said good-by to the man that ran the bus and went with Dad.

Dad let Dan ring the bell to get Mother. Then Dan hid. Mother said, "Was it you that rang, Dad?"

Dan said, "I did, Mother! I rang the bell! I am back!" Then he said, "I have things for you and Dad. This box is for you. That box is for Dad. And this is my tin chick. It has tin wings and it pecks! Grandma got it for me."

Mother kissed him. So did Dad. Then

Dad said, "Well, Dan, hang your cap on a hook. Pick up your things."

But Dan had run to look for Pam. He yelled, "Pam, Pam, I am back!"

Then Pam yelled to Tim and Jim that Dan was back. She sang this song —

> "Dan is back!
> Look at him run!
> Dan is back!
> We can have fun!"

Tim shot his cap gun. He yelled, "Bang, bang, bang! Dan is back!"

Jim yelled to Bud, "Bud! Dan is back!"

Then Dan took a bat, and Jim pitched to him. Tim yelled, "Catch it, Jim!"

Bud yelled, "Run, Dan, run!"

Pam sang, "Dan is back, Dan is back."

Mother hung Dan's cap on a hook. She set his tin chick on the sill. She picked up his bag.

Dad looked at her and said, "Yes, you can tell that Dan is back."

Fit for a King

Mother had to hang up Dan's wet socks. Pam ran by, and Mother looked at her. She said, " Pam, did you rip your hem ? It looks a bit long. Let me pin it up for you."

"That will be good," said Pam.

Tim and Jim missed Pam. "Let's look for her," said Tim.

"I will go and look in the little shack," said Jim. But Pam was not in the shack.

Tim yelled, "Pam, Pam!"

"I am with Dan's mother," said Pam. "She has to fix my hem. I will be back."

"No, Pam," said Mother. "Do not go back yet. I have rung the lunch bell for Dan.

You can have lunch with him if you wish. Then you can go back."

Dan ran up to them and said, "Will it be a good lunch, Mother?"

Mother said, "Yes, it will be a lunch fit for a king!" Then she sang this song — "Sing, sing, sing — lunch fit for a king!"

So Mother fixed a bit of this and a bit of that on a big dish. The dish had ham, yams, fish, hash, and a wing and a leg on it. "You can have the things that you wish," she said to Pam and Dan.

Pam took this, and Dan took that. Then Pam said, "It was good."

Dan said, "It was fit for a king!"

tablet   jacket

Miss Mills   Miss Cook   Miss King

Things for Dan

Mother said, "Dad, can you let me have a little cash or a check? I have to get things for Dan so he can go to school."

"Do you have to get much?" said Dad.

"Well, his red jacket is no good, and his cap has a rip in it," said Mother.

"And I have to have books and a tablet and a pen," said Dan.

"Did Miss Mills or Miss Cook tell you that you have to have a pen?" said Dad.

"No," said Dan, "but Pam has a pen!"

"Well," said Dad, "If Pam has a pen, you can have a pen, Dan." And he tucked the cash into Mother's bag.

Back to School

Jim and Tim yelled, "Dan, Dan, let's go to school!"

Dan said, "Did the school bus go by? Did the school bell ring?"

"No, not yet," said Jim. "But it will not be long. We will have to run."

Mother said, "Dan, do you have your books and pen and tablet?"

"Yes, I do," said Dan, "but I have to get my jacket and cap."

"And your lunch box," said Mother.

Dan ran to get his things. He looked into his lunch box. It had good things in it. It had a fig bun and a little bag of nuts. Dan took his things.   Then he ran to catch up with Jim and Tim.

At school, Tim said, "The school bus did not go by us yet!   Look, Jim, the bus is back of us!"

"And the school bell has not rung," said Jim.   "That's good."

Pam was at school.   She ran to them and said, "Is Miss Mills back?"

"Yes, she is," said Dan.   "My mother said so."

"That's good," said Tim.   "We have fun with Miss Mills.   She lets us run and tag. And she lets us sing."

"She lets us hop, and she tells us a story if we wish," said Jim.

"Yes, Miss Mills lets us do lots of things that are fun," said Pam. "We are in luck to have her!"

Then the school bell rang. Dan and Pam and Jim and Tim ran in to have fun with Miss Mills. But Dan and Pam did not have Miss Mills. Dan had Miss Cook, and Pam had Miss King. Jim and Tim had Miss Mills.

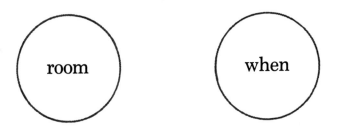

room   when

chicken   kitten   kitchen

Rags at School

When Dan was in school, Rags missed him. He looked in Dan's bedroom for him. He looked in the kitchen. Then Rags went to school to look for Dan. He ran into Miss King's room.

Pam said, "Miss King, that's Dan's pet! That's Rags!"

"Go get Dan from Miss Cook's room," said Miss King to Pam.

So Pam went to Miss Cook's room to get Dan. "Dan's pet is in Miss King's room," she said.

"You will have to go back with your pet, Dan," said Miss Cook. "But do not be long.

Dan's Story

Dan sat with Dad in the kitchen. He had the kitten in his lap. "Did things go well in school, Dan?" said Dad.

"Well," said Dan, "Rags did not let me be in school much."

"Tell Dad the story," said Mother.

So Dan said, "I ran to school with Jim and Tim. Then Rags looked for me in Miss King's room. I had to run back to Mother with him. Then I ran back to school, and Rags got in the lunchroom. Then I took him back to Mother. Then I ran back to school. That's my story! To school and back, to school and back!"

"Well," said Dad, "that's a good story!"

fixing

missing

passing

looking

sitting

humming

tapping

didn't

A Song on the Bells

Miss King was sitting in her room at school. She was fixing a set of bells. The school bell had not rung yet.

A little peg was missing from the set of bells. Miss King fixed that with a bit of wood.

Miss Mills was passing by when Miss King was humming a little song. She was tapping it on the bells.

Miss Mills said, "You got that song from TV, didn't you?"

"Yes, I did," said Miss King.

"Pam and Dan can sing it well," Miss Mills said.

"Then let's get them to sing it for the school," said Miss King. "I can tap it on the bells for them."

"Good. I will go look for them," said Miss Mills. But when she was looking for Pam and Dan, the bell rang. "I will look for them at lunch," she said.

At lunch, Pam was in the lunchroom. She was sitting with Dan.

Miss Mills said to them, "When you have had your lunch, look for me in my room. Miss King and I wish to have you sing that cat song for us. Then you can sing it for the school."

This is the song that Pam and Dan sang as Miss King was tapping it on the bells:

Ding, dong, bell,

My cat fell in the well.

It took six big, big men

To get her up, and then—

Ding, dong, bell,

She fell back in the well.

Ding, dong, bell,

We got her from the well.

We got her with a net,

But she looks sad and wet.

Ding, dong, bell,

I have a cat to sell.

mend

bend

send

lend

end

band

sand

hand

fond

pond

wind

Jobs for Mr. Long

Mr. Long had lots of little jobs to do at school. Bang, bang, bang, he went. He was fixing a sandbox for Miss Mills.

"That sandbox looks good, Mr. Long," she said. "It will fit at the end of my room." Then she said, "Do you have the sand for it? If you do not, Miss Lock will lend us a little."

But Mr. Long said, "I can send for sand, or I can get it when I go for lunch. Then I have a little job to do for Miss Cook."

Mr. Long went to a shop that sells bags of sand. He got six bags and took them back to school. He had to rip the red bands on the bags of sand. Then the sand ran into the sandbox.

The wind got at a little of the sand. Mr. Long had to bend to get the sand up with his hand. When he got up, he had to rub his back. "Well," he said, "that's that."

Then Mr. Long went to Miss Cook's room to do a job for her. He did not have to fix a sandbox for Miss Cook. He had to mend a box for books in her room.

The Man and the Fish

Pam was in her room at school. Miss King said, "Pam, will you tell us a story?"

"Yes," said Pam. "I will tell you a good fish story."

This is Pam's story.

A man is fishing in a pond. He has a big hook on the end of his fishing rod. A big bug is on the hook.

In the pond is a little fish. It's a sunfish. The sunfish is fond of bugs. It looks at the man's bug. But it can't tell that the bug is on a fishhook. So the fish gets the bug, and the hook gets the fish. Then the man has the fish.

"Well," said Miss King, "that's good, Pam! And I can tell you the things that the man and the bug and the fish said. The man said—

Can you tell if you look

That my rod has a hook?

The bug said—

Did he get me in his hand

When he dug into the sand?

The fish said—

Can you tell that I am fond

Of the bugs in my pond?"

Then Miss King said, "And can you tell me this—

If you have fish in a dish,

Is that good for the fish?"

bent

lent

sent

dent

tent

pants

hunt

here 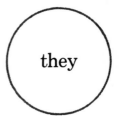they

No Books! No Tablet! No Pen!

"Dan, the school bus is passing by," said Mother. "Here is your jacket, and here is your lunch."

"I am looking for my books and my tablet and my pen," said Dan.

Mother went to look in the kitchen. No books! No tablet! No pen! Then Dan went into the kitchen. "Here is my pen," he said. "It was in my tan pants, but the pants are in the suds! My pen will be no good!"

"Well, I will lend my red pen to you," said Mother. "Go hunt for your books and your tablet!"

Then Mother sent Dan up to his room to hunt for his things. Dan went and looked.

Then he yelled, "Here they are, Mother! My books and my tablet are up here! But Rags has had them! My tablet is bent, and my red book has a dent in it! Miss Cook will be mad."

Mother went to Dan's room. She said, "You will have to tell Miss Cook that Rags did it. And from here on, you will have to check up on your things so that Rags can't get at them."

"But I can't, Mother," said Dan. "Rags hunts and hunts till he gets to them."

"Well, Dan," Mother said, "look here at this bench. It can be locked. Rags can't get at your things if they are in here."

"Good!" said Dan. Then Mother lent her pen to him, and he went to school.

Miss Cook was not mad when she looked at Dan's tablet and his red book, but she said, "Rags is a good pet, Dan, but can't you fix things so that he can't get at your school books?"

"I can from here on," said Dan. "I have a bench with a lock on it. If my things are in the bench, Rags can hunt and hunt, but he can't get at them!"

Let's Go Fishing

Dad is fond of hunting and fishing. So are Gus and Sid. Dad said to them, "Let's go fishing!"

"Good!" said Gus. "And let's have a gun with us. We can look for the fox that took Ben's hen."

So Dad and Sid and Gus went into the woods by a little path. They had guns and fishing rods and a tent with them. They had pots and pans to cook in.

At the end of the path, Dad said, "We can pitch the tent here. That will be my job. I will set the tent up."

Gus said, "And I will look for wood and cook lunch."

Sid said, "I will go fishing. I will get a sunfish or a big bass. Then Gus can cook it."

But Dad did not get the tent up. He said, "I can't pitch this tent. The tent pegs are so little!"

"Well," said Gus, "I have looked and looked for wood, but I have not had much luck. This wood is wet!"

Then Sid yelled, "Look! My fishing rod is bent! Here is the fish for lunch!"

But it was not a fish. The fishhook on Sid's rod had hooked onto a tin can that had a dent in it. Sid tugged on his rod. Then zip! The can went up and up into the sky. Then into the cooking pot it fell!

Sid was sad. He said, "I can't catch a fish."

And Gus was sad. "I can't cook a tin can," he said. "And I can't cook the things we took with us. The wood is wet."

And Dad was sad. "I can't pitch the tent with such little pegs," he said.

So Gus and Sid and Dad packed up the guns and the rods and the pots and pans. Then they went back up the path.

Mother was in the kitchen when they got back. She cooked chicken wings and chicken legs for them. The men said, "We didn't have much luck in the woods, Dot. But we did have good luck here in your kitchen!"

sink	bank
pink	sank
think	tank
ink	thank

bunk

junk

Mrs.   who   purr

along   belong   began   under

Mr. Benton   ribbon

The Kitten's Story

Here I am, a little kitten, sitting in my box under the kitchen sink. I belong to Pam. She sets a little pink dish in the box for me. I think it will be good to lap from it.

"Thank you," I purr to Pam.

My mother is a big cat. She gets fish in her dish. I am little, so I do not get fish yet.

Here is Pam. She lets me sit on her lap. She lets me run along with her. It's fun to do.

I think that Pam is bending to get me. Yes, she is picking me up. She has a pink ribbon for my neck. She thinks I am a doll!

"Pam, Pam," I wish to tell her, "I am not

a doll! I do not wish to have a ribbon on my neck! Set me on the mat. Then we can have fun. I can run and tag you, and you can tag me."

I think Pam can tell that I do not wish to have a ribbon on me. She began to fix it on me, then she let me go. I purr and purr. I rub her leg to tell her, "Thank you so much, Pam!"

At the Pet Shop

Mr. Benton, Jim and Tim's dad, had to cash a check to get bunk beds for them. When he and Mrs. Benton went to the bank, Jim and Tim went with them. They had to pass a pet shop to get to the bank. In the pet shop was a big tank of fish.

"I wish we had a tank of fish," said Tim to Jim.

"You can have fish if you wish," his dad said.

"And a tank?" said Jim.

"If it's a little tank," said his mother.

So they began to look for a little tank for fish. They looked in the pet shop, but the man who ran it did not have a little fish tank.

So Mr. Benton said, "I will go to the bank. You and Mother can look for a tank in the junk shop that we passed."

The junk shop did have a little tank to sell. Jim took it back to the pet shop.

"Can you get me that big red fish?" he said to the man in the shop.

The man had to dip into the tank to get the red fish for Jim. Then he had to get a pink fish for Tim.

Mrs. Benton picked up a box with six pink shells in it. She let them sink into the tank along with a little sand. "Look!" she said. "The shells sank into the sand a bit. I think they look good!"

"So do I," said Tim.

"And so do I!" said Jim. "Thank you for the fish and the shells, Mother!"

"And for the tank!" said Tim.

By then Mr. Benton was back. He had ink on his hand. He said, "The pen at the bank was no good." Then he said to Mrs. Benton, "When will we get the beds?"

"Well, not when we have a fish tank with us!" said Mrs. Benton.

Who Am I?

Pam and Dan and Kim had fun at lunch. Pam looked in her book and said, "Who am I? Can you tell? I am as big as a little bus. My legs are fat. I can pick up a man and set him on my back. Then the man can hunt in the woods. I got here on a ship. The ship had a shed for me. Lots of men fixed the shed. They fed nuts to me. Who am I?"

Kim said, "I can tell!" And she did.

Then Dan said, "Can you tell who I am? I am little, and my mother is a cat. She has fish in a dish, but I lap from a pan. I have a little box for a bed. I purr and purr when Pam lets me sit on her lap and pats me. Who am I?"

Who did Pam think it was?

Then Kim said, "Who am I? My mother is a hen. I am in a big pen with her. I peck at the bugs in the pen. A fox got in the pen and got a hen, but the man took his gun and got the fox. I am little. Who am I? Can you tell?"

Dan said, "I can tell!" And he did.

Who do you think it was?

last	best
fast	rest
past	test
	pest
must	west
just	nest
dust	vest
	chest
fist	
list	

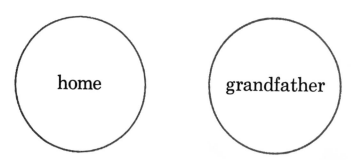

home   grandfather

The Test

At school Miss Cook said, "We must have a test. It will not be bad if you can add. I will do a little of the test with you. Then just do your best, and you will do well."

So Miss Cook took the list and did a bit with them. Then they did the rest.

Kim was fast and did the test well.

Dan was last, and he said, "That test was a pest!"

Miss Cook looked at Dan's test. She said, "Your test is not so bad, Dan, but you did miss six and six."

"Well," said Dan, "I did my best!"

A Hen and Her Nest

Dan and Dad went into the woods. Dad said, "Look! That's a robin's nest! A robin just went into it."

"Let's go up and look in," said Dan.

"No," said Dad. "The robin will not let us. A hen on a nest is just as bad! Let me tell you a story of a hen and her nest."

This is the story that Dad told Dan.

When I was ten, we went west to my grandfather's ranch. He was a big man and he had a big home. He had a pond with fish in it. He had lots of horses.

My grandmother had a lot of chickens on the ranch. She was fond of her big red hen.

58

When I was at the ranch, the hen had a nest with six eggs in it. She was sitting on the nest to hatch her eggs. A fox ran past me and got into the chicken shack. I yelled to Grandfather, "A fox just got into the chicken shack!"

Grandfather shook his fist and ran for his shotgun. He had shells for the gun in his vest.

We ran to the shack. The red hen was hitting the fox with her big wings. She did not let him kill her or get her eggs.

"Look at the dust," I yelled.

Grandfather shot the fox, and the hen got back on her nest. She was bad luck for that fox!

The Shopping List

Jim and Tim's mother had a long shopping list. She said to Mr. Benton, "Dad, we have to go shopping for lots of things, and we must get beds for Jim and Tim." So they took Jim and Tim and went to look at bunk beds for them.

Mr. Benton said, "We must test them. Jim, go up the ladder to the top bed."

So Jim went up to the top bed and had a bit of a rest. When he got back to his mother and dad, Tim went up.

"The bunk beds will be good to get," said Mrs. Benton. "And a chest is good for lots of things. This big chest looks best to me."

So they got the beds and a chest to match.
Then the man in the shop said, "Do you
wish to look at a rug for the bedroom? I
sell rugs here."

"No, thank you," said Mrs. Benton. "I
do not think that I have a rug on my list.
Let me look."

This is the list that she had:

√ Beds
√ Chest
  Socks
  Pants
  Jackets
  Vest for Dad
  Tablet for Tim
  Red pen
  Lunch box
  Dust mop
  Pink ribbon

"Well," said Mrs. Benton, "I have lots of things on my shopping list, but I do not have a rug on it."

"Good-by, then," said the man. "I will send the beds and the chest to you in my van. Good luck with your list!"

mask   lift   help

ask   gift

held

desk   left

disk   next

kept

very

number   seven   dinner

Help From Mr. Long

Dan was in his room at school. He was sitting at his desk. The school bell had not rung yet.

Miss Cook said, "Dan, I have to look for Miss King. Will you ask Mr. Long to get the box of number disks from the next room for me? When the bell rings, we will do numbers with them."

Miss Cook left her room, and Dan went into the next room. "I think I can get that box of disks," he said. But the box that held the disks was very big. It fell with a big bang!

So then Dan said, "I will have to ask Mr. Long to help me. I can't lift that big box!"

But Mr. Long was not in his room. So Dan went back to the box and began to tug at it. Just then Mr. Long passed by.

"Let me lift that box for you, Dan," he said. "You can't lift it."

They took the box into Miss Cook's room, and Mr. Long said, "I think I will just sit at this desk and do my numbers! We didn't have number disks in my school when I was six!" So Mr. Long began to do numbers for fun.

Just then Miss Cook came back to her room. "Thank you, Dan," she said, "for getting the disks for me."

"I didn't get them," said Dan. "Mr. Long did. Thank him, not me!"

A Gift for Pam

"It will not be long till Pam is seven," said Pam's mother to her dad. "Let's look for a gift for her."

"Let's get her a desk," said Pam's dad. "I think she did ask for that."

"Yes," said her mother. "That's just the thing. It can be kept in her room."

At the shop, Pam's dad asked, "Do you sell desks here?"

"Yes," said the man in the shop. "We have a number of desks in the next room. I will go along with you to look at them. I think I can help you."

The last desk that they looked at was the best. It was a desk with a top that

66

lifts up. It had lots of little bins under the top.

"If Pam has this desk, she will not have to hunt for her things," Pam's mother said. "Here are little bins for pens and things. Here is a nook for books. I think this desk will match Pam's bed and chest very well." Then she said to the man in the shop, "We will have this desk."

The man said, "Thank you very much. I will have it sent home for you."

Then Pam's mother said, "I wish I had a big red ribbon for the desk. It's a gift."

"Here is a red ribbon!" said the man.

When he had fixed the ribbon on the desk, Pam's dad said, "That desk is a good gift! It's just the thing for Pam!"

Fun With Masks

Pam's dad and mother left her at Dan's when they went shopping. Dan and Pam had lots of fun till they got back.

Pam fixed a mask for Dan, and Dan fixed a mask for Pam. Dan's mask was a fox, and Pam's was a duck. Then they fixed masks for Rags and Nat. But Rags and Nat didn't wish to have masks, so they ripped them. Then Rags hid the masks.

Just then Pam's mother rang the bell. "Thank you, Dot," she said, "for letting Pam be here. But we have to rush home. I must get dinner." Then she looked for Pam. "Who is that?" she said. "Is it a duck?"

"No!" said Pam. "It's me!"

belt   jump

felt   lump

melt   bump

              mumps

milk

silk   camp

              lamp

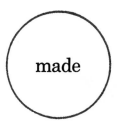
made

better   letter   until

A Doll for Pam

When Pam was seven, she got the desk as a gift from her mother and dad. Her grandmother sent her a doll.

Pam sat at her desk and began a letter. She was thinking, "I will tell Grandma that this is my best doll." Just then the bell rang. Pam jumped up and ran to look. It was Grandma and Grandpa with a big box!

Grandpa said, "Pam, we made things for your doll, but they didn't fit into the little box with her. Your grandma felt so sad that we got the last bus from home, and here we are! Lift the lid of this box."

Pam looked in the box. Then she said, "Mother, look at the things for my doll!

70

Here is a red silk jacket with a belt in the back! And here is a red silk hat."

Grandma said, "The last things are the best, Pam. Grandpa made them for you. Here is a doll bed and a chest to match."

And Pam said, "And here is a little lamp to go on the chest! Thank you very much, Grandma and Grandpa!"

Pam kissed them, and Grandma said she felt much better. "You have your doll," she said, "and the doll has its things."

At last Pam had to go up to bed. She went to the kitchen for her milk. Then she took the doll and its things up to her room. She set them on her desk and said, "I will fix them so that I can look at them when I am in bed." And she did.

Bumps and Lumps

Dan felt a bit sick. Then he began to get little bumps on him. Mother said, "I think you have chicken pox. That's not as bad as mumps. You can't go to school, but you do not have to be in bed."

Dan's rash made him itch, but he had fun at home. He made a little camp in his room, and he made a tent on his bed. He and Rags got under the tent.

Then Dan said, " Rags, you are my ranch horse. Go fast."

But when Rags began to jump, Dan fell from the bed. Mother ran up to look at him. He had bumps from the chicken pox and a big lump on his leg.

Mother took Rags to the kitchen with her, and Dan sat on his bed until he felt better. Then he had lunch. At the end of lunch, Mother passed a big dish to him. " Do not let this melt," she said.

Dan did not let it melt. When he passed the dish back to Mother, he said, " That must be good for chicken pox ! I am better ! "

plan	black
plant	blank
	blanket
plum	
plump	bled

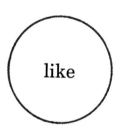

Janet

A Good Plan

Dad had a good plan. He said, "I will dig a pit next to the kitchen, Dot. Then I will set this plant in it. When the plant gets big, it will have plums on it. Dan and I like plums very much."

Mother said, "So do I."

But Dad is getting plump, and he can't bend to dig. So he sat on a blanket and began digging. Then he cut his hand on a little black rock. It bled a lot, and so Mother rushed him to the doctor.

The doctor made Dad sit on a bench and rest his hand on the desk. He got his kit and fixed the cut. Then he said to Dad, "Your hand will get better, but tell Dan to dig for you. You bled a lot, and you will have to rest."

Dad looked blank, but he did as the doctor said. He had Dan dig the little pit and then set the plant in it. When Dan and Dad and Mother had dinner, Dad said to Mother, "Dan did a very good job. He digs better than I do."

Good, Better, Best

Dan did a good job when he helped Dad dig a pit and set a plant in it. Mother hugged him and said, "You did such a good job with Dad's plant that I have made up a little song you can sing."

Here is Mother's song for Dan.

I did a good job.
Then I did it better
At last, I did it best.

My mother said to me,
"Good, better, best,
Do not let it rest,
Till the good is better,
And the better is best."

Pink Plum Punch

Little Janet is in school with Jim and Tim Benton. She went home from school to have lunch with them.

Jim said, "Here is your milk, Janet."

But Janet did not like milk. She said she felt sick when she had milk for lunch.

Mrs. Benton did not wish Janet to get sick, so she made this plan. She took a bit of punch and mixed it with the milk. The punch was made from plums, and it made Janet's milk pink.

"I think you will like this pink punch," said Mrs. Benton.

Janet took a sip of the pink milk. "I do like pink punch! Thank you!" she said.

78

clap	clock
class	clop
clip	club
click	cluck
	clutch

day
play

Linda

The Class Play

Miss Mills began to plan for the class play. She said, "Janet, you can be the hen. Pick seven chickens from the class. Linda, you can be the kitten. Bud, you can be the pig. Jim and Tim, you can be the horse. When you go home, ask your mother to lend you a blanket."

When he got home, Jim asked his mother for a blanket for the play.

She said, "Yes, you can have the black blanket for the day of the play."

It was not a very good blanket. Jim and Tim had played with it at home. They had made a tent with it. The next day they took it to school.

80

Miss Mills fixed the blanket on Jim and Tim. She had a horse mask for them. The blanket and the mask made them look just like a big black horse. But Jim had to clutch the blanket so that it didn't shift when he ran.

Jim and Tim began to run and yell, " Clip-clop! Clip-clop! "

Janet and her chickens said, "Cluck, cluck."

Linda said, "Purr, purr. I am a little kitten."

Bud went, " Unk, unk ! I am a fat pig."

Then the rest of the class began to clap.

Mr. Long was in the room just then. He was fixing the clock for Miss Mills. He made the hands of the clock go. The clock said, "Click, click." And then it said, "Tick-tock, tick-tock."

The class began to clap for Mr. Long and the clock. Mr. Long said, "This is not like a classroom. I think that it's just a fun club!"

slap

slacks

sled

slid

slim

slip

slot

slush

Mr. Dennis

At the Letter Box

Dan's mother got up from her desk. "I must get this letter into the box," she said. "Will you do it for me, Dan? You can go on your sled."

So Dan got his things on. He was very slim, but he did not look it. He had on a thick jacket. Under that, he had a vest. He had thick red mittens with a cap that matched. His slacks made his legs look very plump.

Dan tucked the letter into his jacket and got on his sled. He slid from the top of the little hill to the letter box.

At the letter box was a lot of slush. It made Dan slip when he went to get the letter into the slot. He slid and sat in the slush. It was a good thing he had on slacks and a thick jacket and mittens.

Dan got up and began to slap at his pants to get rid of the slush. Just then Mr. Dennis was passing by the box. He had his letter bag on his back. So he picked up Dan's letter and tucked it into his bag.

Then Dan ran up the hill with his sled. He was very wet when he got home.

The Pup and the Sled

The next day, Linda went sledding with Janet. They slid from the top of the hill on Linda's sled.

Linda's pup began to run along with the sled. It nipped at her slacks and it tugged at her jacket. It did not like her to be on the sled.

Linda slapped at the pup, but it did not let go of her jacket. The sled went very fast, and the jacket began to rip. Then Linda fell into the slush. But Janet kept on the sled.

"You are very bad," said Linda to her pup. "Do you think I like to have slush on me? And you have made a rip in my jacket! Just for that, we will have to go home!" So Linda and her pup went home.

spank

spend

spent

speck

spell

spin

spill

spot

spun

lucky   inky

The Kitten and the Top

Pam was looking at the doll she got from Grandma and Grandpa. Her mother said to them, "You didn't have to spend so much!"

"We spent very little," said Grandma. "We made the doll's things, and it was fun."

Then Grandpa said to Pam, " Here is a gift you can have for Dan. Look, it's a black top with red spots. But when I spin it fast, the red spots look like a ribbon."

Pam's kitten ran past as he spun the top. The kitten began to bat at the top. When the top did not spin so fast, the red specks did not look like a red ribbon.

At last the top fell. It hit the kitten. Then the kitten ran and hid.

The Inky Kitten

When Pam went to school, the kitten got into her bedroom. It jumped from the sill to the desk. Then it hit the ink on the desk. The ink began to spill on the rug. It made a big, black spot.

At lunch, Pam went up to her room to get a spelling book. "Mother! Mother!" she yelled. "Look at my room!"

Mother ran to look.

Pam said, "I will have to spank that kitten. She did this."

"No," said her mother. "You did not shut your kitten in the kitchen when you left for school. You must not spank the kitten, and you are lucky that I do not spank you."

Just then the kitten ran past them. It had ink spots on it.

"My, but that's an inky kitten!" Pam's mother said.

"Here, Inky. Here, Inky," said Pam.

The kitten ran to Pam, and she did a good job on its spots with a rag. Then the kitten had no ink spots left on it. But it ran to Pam when she said, "Here, Inky!"

stand

stack

stem

step

stiff

stick

still

stitch

sting

stop

stuck

Help for Mr. Dennis

Mr. Dennis was sick with a stiff back, and he had to be in bed. He did not go with his letter bag to homes for days and days. At last he was back on his job.

He was standing at the letter box when Tim and Jim went running by. They stopped next to him and said, " Can we help you, Mr. Dennis ? "

" Yes, I think so," said Mr. Dennis, " if you will just stand still by my bag. I have to get the letters from the box. Then I have to fill my bag with them."

A thick letter was stuck in the box. Jim got a little stick for Mr. Dennis. It helped him get the letter that was stuck.

Then Mr. Dennis began to stack the letters in his bag.   Six or seven letters fell from it.

"My bag has a big rip in it," said Mr. Dennis.   "Mrs. Dennis will have to stitch it when I get home."

Tim picked up the letters and stuck them into the bag for Mr. Dennis.

"Well, Tim and Jim, you did help me very much," said Mr. Dennis.   "I still can't bend to pick things up.   Thank you a lot!"

Mr. Dennis went along with his bag.   Then Tim took big steps like Mr. Dennis and said, "I think I will be a letter man when I am big."

"So will I," said Jim.

Good Luck for Sid

Sid was on a stepladder picking plums. He had the last big red plum by the stem as Mr. Dennis was passing by. Mr. Dennis stopped and looked up at Sid. Then he said, "A bad bug is on your neck, Sid! Stand still, or it will sting you!"

But Sid slapped at the bug. Then the ladder began to slip. Mr. Dennis rushed to the ladder and held it.

"That was a bad spot to be in," he said to Sid. "Did the bug sting you?"

Sid felt his neck. "No," he said, "it didn't. And I was in luck not to get killed on that stepladder. Here, have a plum, Mr. Dennis, with my thanks!"

skin   swam

skip

                      swim

skunk   swing

twins

twig

bigger   biggest

The Swing

The twins, Jim and Tim, got a swing to play on. Jim is a bit bigger than Tim, but Tim can swing just as well as Jim.

Little Bud rushed to Jim and Tim's to play on the swing. So did Janet and Linda. Bud had fun. He went up and up into the sky. Then Linda said, "Me next!" And Janet said, "Then me!"

Linda and Bud and Janet kept swinging and swinging. But Jim and Tim just looked. Then Linda rubbed her leg on the swing and made a cut in the skin. She went home, and so did Janet and Bud.

Then Jim said to Tim, "Let's swing!" The twins got on the swing, and up they went!

In the Woods

Jim and Tim are not six yet. Ted is past ten. Jim is a little bigger than Tim, and Ted is the biggest. He is much bigger than Jim and Tim.

Ted belongs to a Cub Pack. Jim said to him, "Can we go into the woods with you on the next good day?"

"Yes," said Ted, "but you will have to do as I tell you."

"We will!" said the twins.

So Ted took Jim and Tim into the woods with him when he went the next day. Jim began to skip along the path, but Ted made him stop. "It's not a good thing to skip in the woods," he said. "This path has lots of twigs and rocks on it. You can skin your leg if you skip here."

Just then Tim yelled, "Ted! Look at the black cat! Can I pat him?"

"Stand still!" said Ted. "That's not a cat! It's a skunk!"

The twins did stand very still, and the skunk left.

Next, Ted took Jim and Tim to look at the pond. "My Cub Pack swims here," he said.

But Tim said, "Look! A fish! It just swam past me!"

"Can I catch a fish for my fish tank?" Jim asked Ted.

"No," said Ted. "They do not let us fish in this pond."

"Then let's go home," said Jim to Ted. "I can't skip. Tim can't pat the black cat. And you will not let me catch a fish for my fish tank!"

"Yes, let's go home," said Tim. "We can play on the swing and have fun!"

"Well," said Ted, "we had better go home if you can't do as I tell you."

So he took the twins home and left them playing on the swing. Then he went back into the woods.

crack   Fred

crash

crab   Frank

crib   frog

crisp

crust

crush

bunny   funny   cooky

himself

Is It Better?

Crash, bang! Crash, bang! Mrs. Dennis was fixing crab cutlets for lunch. She had to crack the crab shell to do it. Then she crushed the crab into little bits.

As the lunch was cooking, she went to look into the crib. It was lucky she did. Little Frank was standing up in his crib and yelling.

Mrs. Dennis took Frank to the kitchen with her. She had a cooky for him that looked just like a rabbit and a cooky that looked like a funny pink frog.

When the crab cutlets had cooked, Mrs. Dennis said to Mr. Dennis, "Fred, lunch is fixed. Let's sit and have it when it's hot."

The cutlets had a crust that looked good and crisp. Mr. Dennis had a cutlet. Then he had a bunny cooky.

Mrs. Dennis said, "Do you like the bunny cooky better or the frog cooky?"

Mr. Dennis said, "I can't tell." He took a frog cooky. "I still can't tell," he said. So he took a bunny cooky. "I just can't tell if this is better than that."

Then Mr. Dennis began to play with little Frank. At last he took him back to his crib for a nap. He felt like napping himself, but he had to go back to his job.

When he left, he tucked a frog cooky and a bunny cooky into his bag. "I will tell you when I get home if I like this cooky better or that," he said to Mrs. Dennis.

drop	bring	track
	brick	
drip		trick
drink	bran	
	brand	truck
dress		trunk

drum

herself	we'll	saddle

Lots of Slush

Janet had left home to go to school. The slush was melting—drip, drip, drip. It made Janet slip, and she fell into a patch of slush. Her dress had big wet spots on it.

"I can't go to school looking like this," she said to herself. She ran home to tell her mother.

Janet's mother looked at the spots and said, "No, you can't go to school in that dress. Go up to your room and get your good red dress. I think I packed it in the trunk."

But Janet's red dress had a rip in it. She looked at the rip and began to cry. "I can't go to school!" she said. "That dress has spots on it, and this dress has a rip!"

Mother got her mending kit. "Hush, Janet," she said. "Bring the dress to me. I will try to stitch the rip."

Mother stitched the rip in a rush, but the dress looked a lot better. "Here, get it on and run along to school," she said.

But just as Janet got to school, a big truck filled with bricks slid on the slush. It made wet tracks, and big drops of slush got on Janet's red dress.

Janet looked and said. "Well, I just can't help it! I have to go to school, slush or no slush!" So she went on into school. She got to her room just as the bell began to ring.

Lucky, the Ranch Horse

Dan was telling Dad a story he had looked at on TV. This is the story.

Lucky is the biggest horse on the Bell Ranch. He is bigger than Jet, and he is kept in a pen by himself.

Lucky belongs to Mr. Bellman. He can run very fast, so Mr. Bellman made a track for him. He took the big horse to the track in a truck. On the truck was the Bell Ranch brand. The brand is a little bell.

Ed, a man at the track, began to get a saddle on Lucky. It made the big horse mad! He began to pitch and buck, but Ed held on to him.

Mr. Bellman ran to the truck. When he got back, he had Lucky's lunch in a big box that looked like a drum. The lunch was bran mash. Mr. Bellman fed Lucky, and the horse stopped bucking to have his lunch. Next Lucky had a drink.

By then, Ed had the saddle on Lucky and was up on his back! But Lucky did not run very fast. "It's the lunch that did it," said Ed. "The next day that we try this, we'll have to think of a trick to get the saddle on him. We must not let him have his lunch until he has run!"

———————

Then Dan said to Dad, "I can't think of the trick that they will play on Lucky. I will have to look at TV next Sunday so that I can tell you the rest."

TO THE TEACHER

The MERRILL LINGUISTIC READERS series consists of six Readers developed upon linguistic principles applicable to the teaching of reading. Detailed teaching procedures are set forth in the Teacher's Edition of each Reader in the Basic Program.

With a few exceptions, the words introduced in the first four Readers in the series belong to the first major set of spelling patterns: consonant-letter(s)–vowel-letter–consonant-letter(s). All the words introduced in Reader Four are listed on the next four pages, under the headings "Words in Pattern," "Sight Words," and "Applications of Patterning."

The entries under "Words in Pattern" represent additional matrixes (specific letter combinations occurring as constant features) in the first major set of spelling patterns. All five vowel-letters represented in the matrixes of the first three Readers are used in these matrixes, and the words are characterized by consonant-letter clusters in either initial or final position or both. Also presented are forms in the first major set of spelling patterns with the inflectional suffix -*ing*.

Under "Sight Words" are listed a few high-frequency words that are not in the spelling patterns of this Reader or of the three preceding Readers.

Words listed under "Applications of Patterning" are similar in pattern type to words previously introduced or represent combinations of such types.

WORD LISTS

(The lists on pages 109-112 are for teacher reference only. No aspects of these lists should be pointed out or discussed with the students.)

Pages	Words in Pattern	Sight Words	Pages	Words in Pattern	Sight Words
5-10	shop shot ship shut shed shell shack	or from Mr.	32-35	fixing missing passing looking sitting humming tapping	
11-15	fish wish dish rash hash mash cash		36-40	mend bend send lend end band sand hand fond pond wind	
16-21	rang hang sang bang long song ring sing king wing thing hung rung		41-47	bent lent sent dent tent pants hunt	here they
22-26		school	48-55	sink pink think ink bunk junk bank sank tank thank	Mrs. who purr
27-31		room when			

Pages	Words in Pattern	Sight Words	Pages	Words in Pattern	Sight Words
56-62	last fast past must just dust fist list best rest test pest west nest vest chest	home grandfather	69-73	belt felt melt milk silk jump lump bump mumps camp lamp	made
63-68	mask ask desk disk lift gift left next kept help held	very	74-78	plan plant plum plump black blank blanket bled	like
			79-82	clap class clip click clock clop club cluck clutch	day play

Pages	Words in Pattern	Sight Words
83-86	slap slacks sled slid slim slip slot slush	
87-90	spank spend spent speck spell spin spill spot spun	
91-94	stand stack stem step stiff stick still stitch sting stop stuck	

Pages	Words in Pattern	Sight Words
95-99	skin skip skunk swam swim swing twins twig	
100-102	crack crash crab crib crisp crust crush Fred Frank frog	
103-107	drop drip drink dress drum bring brick bran brand track trick truck trunk	

Applications of Patterning

(The numbers are page numbers.)

5-10	32-35	56-62	74-78 cont.	95-99
ketchup	didn't	add	helped	bigger
good-by	ding	robin's	hugged	biggest
woodshed	dong	robin	mixed	swinging
shells	sell	grandfather's	Janet's	rubbed
ships		chickens		Ted
tots		Grandfather		belongs
nutmeg	36-40	shook	79-82	Cub Pack
matchbox	jobs	shotgun	Linda	twigs
Mr. Woods	Mr. Long	hitting	played	swims
	sandbox	shopping	shift	playing
	Miss Lock	ladder	unk	
11-15	sells	jackets	hands	100-102
codfish	bands		tick-tock	bunny
yam	fishing		classroom	funny
packed	rod	63-68		cooky
grandma	sunfish	number		himself
grandpa	man's	seven	83-86	cutlets
	fishhook	dinner	Mr. Dennis	crushed
		disks	mittens	yelling
16-21		rings	matched	rabbit
things	41-47	numbers	sledding	cutlet
wings	hunts	getting	Linda's	napping
hook	till	asked	nipped	
hem	hunting	desks	slapped	103-107
missed	rods	lifts		herself
yams	bass	nook		we'll
	hooked	ripped	87-90	saddle
	onto	letting	lucky	melting
22-26	tugged	rush	inky	cry
tablet	cooking		doll's	mending
jacket			spots	hush
Miss Mills		69-73	specks	try
Miss Cook	48-55	better	spelling	stitched
Miss King	along	letter	Inky	bricks
books	belong	until		tracks
	began	thinking		drops
	under	jumped	91-94	Lucky
27-31	Mr. Benton	bumps	homes	telling
chicken	ribbon	lumps	days	Mr. Bellman
kitten	kitten's	pox (chicken)	standing	Ed
kitchen	bending		running	Lucky's
bedroom	picking		stopped	bucking
Miss King's	thinks	74-78	letters	Sunday
Miss Cook's	doll	Janet	steps	
songs	Kim	plums	stepladder	
lunchroom		digging	killed	
		rushed	thanks	